Monsieur Roscoe
In the City

Jim Field

At the very top of a very tall building lives a friendly dog called Monsieur Roscoe and his goldfish, Fry.

Bonjour Monsieur Roscoe! Bonjour Fry!

It's Fry's birthday today! Monsieur Roscoe has made her
a birthday breakfast and bought her some snazzy new glasses.

Joyeux anniversaire Fry!

Joyeux anniversaire !
Happy birthday!

Monsieur Roscoe is planning a birthday surprise for his friend . . .
a picnic party in the park! There's lots to get ready.
First, time to bake!

des œufs
eggs

du sucre
sugar

de la farine
flour

un fouet
whisk

un bol de mixage
mixing bowl

du lait
milk

une cuillère
spoon

de la crème
cream

du beurre
butter

du chocolat
chocolate

un couteau
knife

Careful with those eggs, Monsieur Roscoe!

Voilà! The birthday cake is ready. Now Monsieur Roscoe just needs to pick up a few more things for the picnic.

des citrouilles
pumpkins

des brocolis
broccoli

des poireaux
leeks

des pommes de terre
potatoes

des carottes
carrots

des choux
cabbages

des tomates
tomatoes

des concombres
cucumbers

They stop at the greengrocer. Monsieur and Madame Meadow have the best fruit in town.

des raisins
grapes

des fraises
strawberries

des cerises
cherries

des citrons
lemons

des poires
pears

des bananes
bananas

des oranges
oranges

des pommes
apples

des pastèques
watermelons

Look at those juicy red strawberries. Fry's favourite!

Monsieur Roscoe finds everything he needs for the picnic.
But wait . . . where is Fry?

Monsieur Roscoe looks up . . . and down . . . and all around . . .

but Fry is nowhere to be seen! Where is she?

Suddenly, Monsieur Roscoe's friend Wilma spots something. Oh no, Fry is floating away!

Regardes lá-bas !
Look over there!

Allons-y !
Let's go!

The chase is on! But – oh dear! – the city centre is very crowded.
Monsieur Roscoe and Wilma can't see Fry anywhere.

une
statue
statue

**un kiosque
à journaux**
newspaper stand

Jouets

un magasin de jouets
toy shop

un passage piéton
pedestrian crossing

un jongleur
juggler

SNAX

POMME

HATS

Supermarché

BUS TOURS BUS TOURS

un supermarché
supermarket

l'hôtel de ville
town hall

un feu de
circulation
traffic lights

un plan de ville
city map

VILLE

METRO

le métro
underground

un vendeur de ballons
balloon seller

"Has anyone seen a floating fish?"
asks Monsieur Roscoe.

That's very helpful . . . but it's *not* Fry.

But wait! Here's Dougal . . . and he's just spotted her!

The three friends hop on Monsieur Roscoe's bike and hurry after Fry. Oh crumbs, she's floating into the Dinosaur Museum!

Inside the museum, Monsieur Roscoe gets a *tiny* bit distracted by the dinosaur bones.

un squelette de baleine
whale skeleton

fossiles
fossils →

toilettes
toilets →

des escaliers
stairs

un guide touristique
tourist guide

Fry keeps on floating up and up and up.
Oh no, someone has left the window open!

The friends race out of the museum . . .
but the wind is blowing Fry further away.

This is no time to hang around!

There's only one thing for it, Monsieur Roscoe. All aboard!

On the bridge, a crowd has gathered to watch.

Is it a bird? Is it a plane?
No, it's a flying fish in a party hat!

High above the city, Fry can see for miles and miles.
The view is very nice . . .

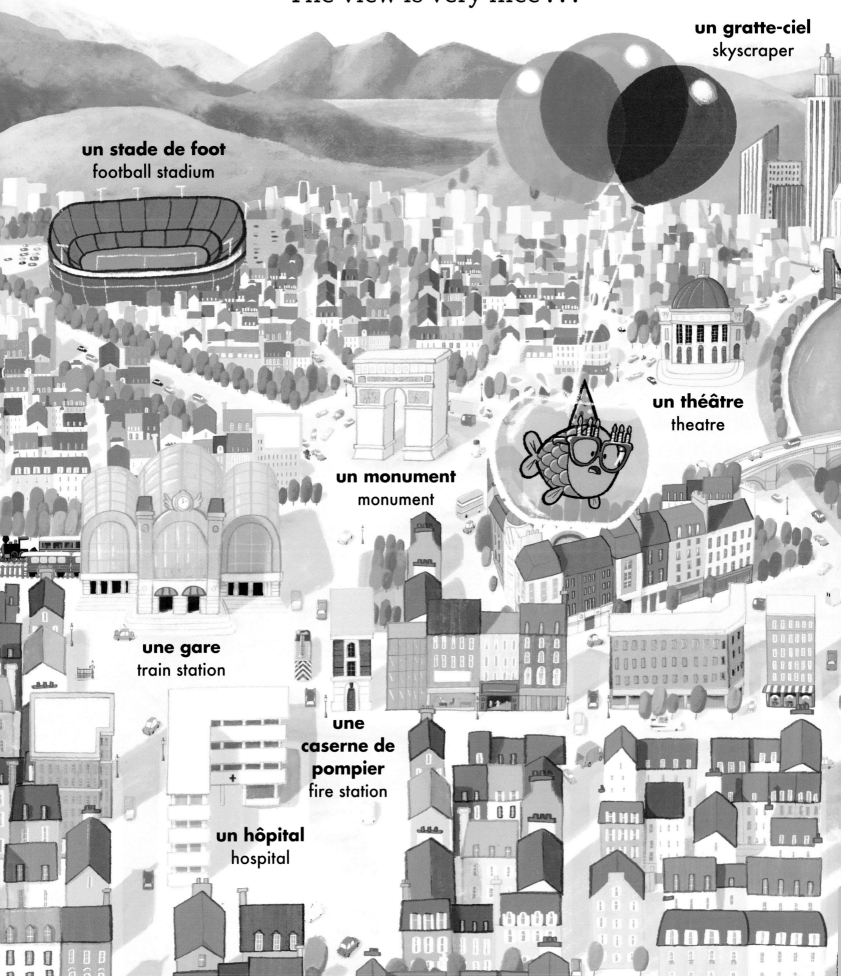

un gratte-ciel
skyscraper

un stade de foot
football stadium

un théâtre
theatre

un monument
monument

une gare
train station

une caserne de pompier
fire station

un hôpital
hospital

but she'd quite like to come back to Earth now.

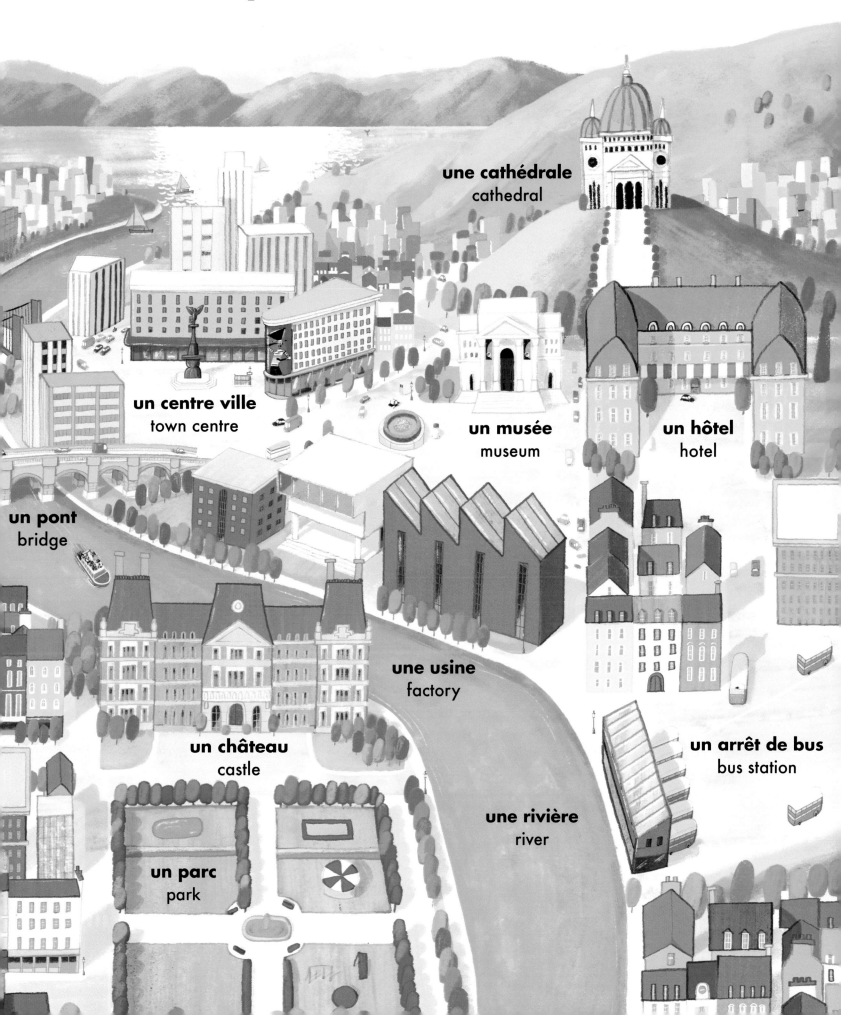

une cathédrale
cathedral

un centre ville
town centre

un musée
museum

un hôtel
hotel

un pont
bridge

une usine
factory

un arrêt de bus
bus station

un château
castle

une rivière
river

un parc
park

Just at that moment . . . POP!
Fry starts to float below the clouds . . .

and down to the rooftops . . . POP!

She drifts on, into the city . . .

and towards the park.
Fry has attracted quite a crowd!

C'est super !
Super!

C'est Super-Poisson !
It's Super-Fish!

La voilà !
There she is!

Incroyable !
Incredible!

BUS TOURS

un étang
pond

un marchand de glace
ice cream stand

une poubelle
bin

Now Fry can see Monsieur Roscoe ...

un skateur
skateboarder

un banc
park bench

une fontaine
fountain

**une partie
de football**
game of football

un bac à sable
sand pit

un carrousel
carousel

un joggeur
runner

. . . and Monsieur Roscoe can see Fry!

un toboggan
slide

un trottoir
footpath

une balançoire
swings

un manège
merry-go-round

Fry looks for a safe place to land . . .

but Monsieur Roscoe is not looking where he is going.

Splash landing!

Yippeeee!
Monsieur Roscoe is so happy to have his friend back.

At last, it's time for the birthday picnic . . . but Fry
seems to have made a LOT of new friends today.

Will there be enough cake for everyone?

It looks like you have a cunning plan, Monsieur Roscoe ...

un sandwich
sandwich

des cookies
cookies

des saucisses
sausages

une pastèque
watermelon

des chips
crisps

une brioche
brioche

une baguette
baguette

des fraises
strawberries

un panier de pique-nique
picnic hamper

un gâteau
cake

Well now, that IS a big cake.
Bravo, Monsieur Roscoe!

Cake all round!
Well done, Monsieur Roscoe.
Fry's birthday has been one that even
a GOLDFISH will never forget!

Monsieur Roscoe and Fry hope you've had fun in the city with them. Can you spot the following items in the book?

AT THE GREENGROCER

- **a ladder**
  une échelle
- **6 yellow ducklings**
  6 canetons jaunes
- **a teddy bear**
  un nounours

IN THE CITY CENTRE

- **2 dinosaur balloons**
  2 ballons dinosaures
- **6 yellow buses**
  6 bus jaunes
- **a zebra**
  un zèbre

AT THE MUSEUM

- **a yellow umbrella**
  un parapluie jaune
- **a volcano**
  un volcan
- **a fossil**
  un fossile

ABOVE THE CITY

- **9 green buses**
  9 bus verts
- **a train**
  un train
- **5 boats**
  5 bateaux

AT THE PARK

- **a cat on a bike**
  un chat à vélo
- **a panda**
  un panda
- **16 pigeons**
  16 pigeons

AT THE PARTY

- **a seagull**
  une mouette
- **a fish balloon**
  un ballon poisson
- **26 party hats**
  26 chapeaux d'anniversaire

HODDER CHILDREN'S BOOKS
First published in Great Britain in 2023 by Hodder and Stoughton

Copyright © Jim Field 2023

The moral rights of the author-illustrator have been asserted.
All rights reserved

A CIP catalogue record for this book is available from the British Library.

ISBN: 978 1 444 95597 2

1 3 5 7 9 10 8 6 4 2

Printed and bound in China

Hodder Children's Books
An imprint of Hachette Children's Group
Part of Hodder and Stoughton
Carmelite House, 50 Victoria Embankment,
London, EC4Y 0DZ
An Hachette UK Company

www.hachette.co.uk
www.hachettechildrens.co.uk

Hodder
Children's
Books

For our darling daughter Lola, who inspired the creation of Monsieur Roscoe.